SING MUSICAL THEATRE

INTERMEDIATE (GRADES 4–5)

WHISTLE DOWN THE WIND

AND 14 OTHER SONGS FROM THE SHOWS

Selected and edited by John Gardyne and Luise Horrocks

© 2011 by Faber Music Ltd and Trinity College London
First published in 2011 by Faber Music Ltd in association with Trinity College London
Bloomsbury House
74–77 Great Russell Street
London WC1B 3DA
Music processed by SEL Engraving
Cover design by Lydia Merrills-Ashcroft
Printed in England by Caligraving Ltd
All rights reserved

CD produced and arranged by Paul Honey
© 2011 by Faber Music Ltd and Trinity College London
℗ 2011 by Faber Music Ltd and Trinity College London

ISBN10: 0-571-53558-5
EAN13: 978-0-571-53558-3

To buy Faber Music or Trinity publications or to find out about the full range of titles available,
please contact your local music retailer or Faber Music sales enquiries:

Faber Music Ltd, Burnt Mill, Elizabeth Way, Harlow, CM20 2HX England
Tel: +44(0)1279 82 89 89   Fax: +44(0)1279 82 89 90
sales@fabermusic.com   fabermusicstore.com

INTRODUCTION

This book contains 15 songs from a wide variety of shows and movies – some very well known, others less so – which offer a range of performing challenges suitable for intermediate-level singing and musical theatre students.

The best musical theatre songs are self-contained playlets in which a character – or a group of characters – in a specific dramatic setting explores an idea, learns something, makes a decision or changes in some way. It is the performer's job to convey this process to the audience with clarity, conviction and understanding.

In order to do this it is essential that the performer knows where the character is, what is happening in the story at that point, who the character is singing to and why s/he is expressing these ideas at that moment. So in the **BACKGROUND** to each song we have provided some key information about plot, characters and the dramatic situation, along with a brief summary of the production history of the musical from which it comes. But these are only the bare bones. There is no substitute for careful, detailed research and we would encourage performers to listen to recordings, attend performances, read librettos and find out as much as they can about these – and other – musicals and the writers and theatre professionals who created them. All this information will feed into your performance and make it richer, more detailed and more rewarding for both you and your audience.

The **PERFORMANCE NOTES** offer some starting points for interpretation and performance. These are intended to offer suggestions and are in no way intended to represent a 'definitive' rehearsal technique. Many of the observations and acting approaches can be applied to other songs in the collection (and indeed elsewhere), so we hope that as students and their teachers explore the different songs in the book they will develop a variety of approaches to preparation and rehearsal which they can apply to a range of repertoire.

In some cases, performers who are singing individual numbers from a show – where the original context may be impossible to recreate or would be too confusing for an audience – may choose to experiment with new approaches and make some innovative performance choices. A solo number might be shared between two or more performers, a duet sung as a solo, a song by a female character be sung by a man or vice versa, or the song re-imagined in a completely different dramatic situation, providing new perspectives and illuminating new meanings in the lyrics. The world of musical theatre has a rich tradition of this process (sometimes referred to as *de-contextualisation*) and we have included some suggestions on this that you might consider. But be careful. However you may re-invent a number – and the possibilities for doing so may be immense – always make sure that all the lyrics make sense and that the song as a whole retains an essential integrity and coherence.

The **SINGING TIPS** provide some technical exercises appropriate to the particular style or demands of each number. We are not suggesting that individual exercises should be used solely in the preparation of that one song and these may prove useful in working on others. Our intention is that over time students will build up a range of techniques which will help them develop their singing along with their acting and movement skills.

The CD contains backing tracks for each of the 15 songs. While these may be used in performance, they are intended primarily as an aid to rehearsal and preparation. Again, tempi and dynamics provide a starting point only and are not intended to be 'definitive'. Performers who have the opportunity to work with a piano accompanist should explore the musical possibilities of each score, which will enable them to further refine and nuance their performances and to make them uniquely personal, uniquely their own.

John Gardyne
Chief Examiner in Drama and Speech Subjects, Trinity College London

Luise Horrocks,
Singing teacher and Associate Chief Examiner, Trinity College London

BRUSH UP YOUR SHAKESPEARE
KISS ME KATE

BACKGROUND

Bella and Sam Spewack's ingenious libretto for *Kiss Me Kate* (1948) interweaves a musical adaptation of Shakespeare's *The Taming of the Shrew* with the backstage story of a struggling theatre company whose survival depends on their production of the show being a success. Each actor plays both a member of the company and a character in the 'play-within-the-play', creating dazzling multi-perspectives as the two stories intertwine. Cole Porter's inspired score is brilliantly integrated with the action, and the show is regarded as one of the most sophisticated musicals ever produced on Broadway.

Fred Graham, the leader of the theatre troupe, is pursued by two gangsters who are chasing him to repay a gambling debt. The gangsters find themselves pressured into joining the company, and on the opening night of *The Taming of the Shrew* they give the audience this piece of advice on how to impress the ladies.

PERFORMANCE NOTES

This is a comic song built around a single joke: but it's a great joke, brilliantly sustained. It is of course utterly absurd that a chance encounter with a theatre troupe has turned these two violent, hard-nosed gangsters into highly erudite experts on classical drama, with the complete works of Shakespeare at their fingertips. While it's not essential to adopt an accent, there's huge comic potential in hearing these sophisticated literary allusions from a tough guy (or gal) with a Bronx or Brooklyn accent.

Remember that you're giving the audience advice on how to 'wow' society girls – so you should aim to wow them too. Relish the witty and at times outrageous rhymes ('flatter 'er / Cleopatterer', 'ambessider / Cressida'). Punch out the first line of each couplet as if challenging the audience to work out which play will be name-checked or quoted at the end of the second line. You'll always be one step ahead. And they'll love it.

SINGING TIPS

This song has to have clear words addressed straight to the audience. Make sure there's always a feeling of energy, with your breath forming part of the rhythm of the song.

Practise taking quick breaths while keeping your throat open and your abdominal muscles working. Think of a surprised breath – inhale through your mouth as if you're surprised and feel the slightly cold air hit the back of your throat. Don't make too much sound though or be tempted to suck the air in.

Try different ways of practising the words. First try whispering them, making sure you remain completely audible. Then try mouthing them. This second exercise works really well if you play a recording of the song, miming to someone else singing. Make sure you breathe in the right places as you mime.

If you can, record yourself singing and listen back to it to make sure all the words are clear, particularly if you choose to adopt an accent.

BRUSH UP YOUR SHAKESPEARE

WORDS AND MUSIC BY COLE PORTER

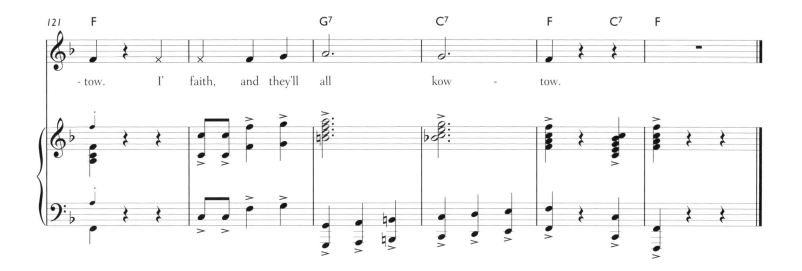

Additional lyrics

Refrain 4:
Brush up your Shakespeare
Start quoting him now
Brush up your Shakespeare
And the women you will wow
Better mention *The Merchant of Venice*
When her sweet pound o' flesh you would menace
If her virtue, at first, she defends – well
Just remind her that *All's Well That Ends Well*
And if still she won't give you a bonus
You know what Venus got from Adonis!
Brush up your Shakespeare
And they'll all kowtow.

Refrain 5:
Brush up your Shakespeare
Start quoting him now
Brush up your Shakespeare
And the women you will wow
If your goal is a Washington Heights dream
Treat the kid to *A Midsummer Night's Dream*
If she then wants an all-by-herself night
Let her rest ev'ry 'leventh or *Twelfth Night*
If because of your heat she gets huffy
Simply play on and "Lay on, MacDuffy!"
Brush up your Shakespeare
And they'll all kowtow.

BUT NOT FOR ME

GIRL CRAZY

BACKGROUND

During the Great Depression, Broadway audiences wanted undemanding escapist entertainment, and shows like *Girl Crazy* (1930) gave it to them. The show's snappy libretto poked light-hearted fun at both city slickers and country bumpkins and – more significantly – provided the vehicle for 14 superb songs by George and Ira Gershwin. Although *Girl Crazy* has rarely been revived on stage in its original form, *Crazy for You* – a significantly revised and rewritten adaptation with several additional songs taken from other shows – ran successfully in New York and London in the early 1990s, bringing the Gershwins' genius to a new generation of theatre-goers.

Misbehaving Manhattan playboy Danny Churchill is sent by his father to sleepy Custerville, Arizona, where there are no nightclubs, no casinos and no dancing girls. Undeterred, Danny turns the town into a swinging dude ranch and gambling emporium. He also falls for the local postmistress Mollie Gray, who initially dismisses his advances but – after various ups and downs – eventually succumbs to his charm and sophistication. In this song Mollie explores her conflicting feelings about Danny.

PERFORMANCE NOTES

When performing the song, it's important that you retain your dignity. Don't wallow in self-pity over an unsuccessful love affair: be – or at least attempt to be – calm, rational, even matter-of-fact as you explain your feelings to the audience. You are, after all, a smart, educated, independent woman. You have a whole armoury of defence mechanisms to keep your emotions under control: unexpected and witty rhymes ('try it / riot', 'Polyannas / bananas'), a knowing reference to Beatrice Fairfax (the first newspaper 'Agony Aunt'), a sly dig at 19th-century classic Russian drama – and, when necessary, you can send yourself up with mock-tragic Shakespearian expressions ('Heigh-ho! Alas! Lack-a-day'). However, the song is underpinned with a deep personal sense of loss, most clearly expressed in the couplet: 'I can't dismiss / The memory of his kiss'.

The second verse implies that 'he' has now found another love, whom he intends to marry. The more you talk about the situation, the more confused your feelings become ('I'm all at sea'). What went wrong? Why couldn't we make it work? Your performance could end on a note of bitterness and betrayal. But it might be more effective to convey a sad acceptance of an unhappy truth, of a missed chance that may never come your way again.

SINGING TIPS

The opening of the song is almost conversational in style but don't be too casual with the singing; make sure you keep the repeated notes crisp and energised.

The chorus contains a number of tricky diphthongs, for example *way* or *day*. Try saying these words slowly out loud to hear and feel how there are two distinct vowel sounds merged into the English sound *ay*. When a diphthong occurs on a longer note you need to think carefully about how to manage the two sounds. With *ay* don't move into the *ee* sound too quickly, or exaggerate the slide between the two sounds. Avoid tightening the cheek muscles and squeezing the *ee*. On one note practise singing *oo – ee – oo*. The lips naturally come forward on the *oo*, but see how far forward you can keep the lips on *ee*.

BUT NOT FOR ME

TRACK 2

MUSIC AND LYRICS BY GEORGE GERSHWIN AND IRA GERSHWIN

Old Man Sun-shine lis-ten, you! Nev-er tell me, "Dreams come true!" Just

try it And I'll start a ri - ot.

CLOSE EVERY DOOR

JOSEPH AND THE AMAZING TECHNICOLOR ® DREAMCOAT

BACKGROUND

Joseph... started life as a 15-minute cantata performed by pupils at a London school in 1968, one of the earliest works of the writing team Andrew Lloyd Webber and Tim Rice. It was gradually expanded and eventually arrived on Broadway in a full production in 1982. Although far more modest in scale and ambition than many of the writers' other musicals, it's a long-time favourite with young performers and to date has received over 20,000 productions by schools and amateur groups.

Based on a story from the Book of Genesis, the musical tells the story of Joseph, the favourite son of Jacob. Joseph's 11 brothers grow jealous of him, steal his multi-coloured coat and sell him as a slave to the Egyptian pharoah Potiphar. When Potiphar's wife makes suggestive advances to Joseph, her husband jumps to conclusions and has him thrown in jail. Degraded and downcast, he sings this number.

PERFORMANCE NOTES

This song comes at Joseph's lowest moment. After the shock of his brothers' betrayal he slowly rebuilt his life in a new land, but has now been imprisoned for a crime he didn't commit. It's a complex situation, so it's important that the audience understand the dramatic context. If you're working without scenery, lights or costume, how are you going to convey the sense of a confined, dark and miserable prison cell? What might it be like in there? Cold? Damp? Unbearably stuffy? Full of scuttling insects? Try various options and then make some positive decisions. And what is your mood going to be at the opening? Despairing? Angry? Exhausted? Frustrated? Decide on that too and commit to it in performance.

Joseph's ideas develop as he sings. Notice how his initial bitterness at his mistreatment turns into something more positive. He realises that he'll find the answers he's seeking because of his suffering. This will bring new meaning not only to his own life, but also to the lives of all the 'Children of Israel'. How might your mood change as you make these new discoveries?

In the show the ensemble and a chorus of children join Joseph on the last chorus. Now the personal 'I have been promised' becomes 'We have been promised'. Even if you're performing the entire song as a solo, explore ways in which you might include your audience in this climactic moment, finishing the number with a triumphant sense of shared hope.

SINGING TIPS

Much of this song is in a minor key. Are you able to identify which one? Try singing up and down the melodic minor scale, carefully listening to the changing 6th and 7th tones on the way up and down. Then try singing the natural minor (where the 6th and 7th are the same ascending and descending). Finally sing up and down the minor arpeggio a few times, checking the minor 3rd.

Now for some work on the higher ranges of this song. Remember that to sing high effectively you need to think low! As you sing through the rising phrases, imagine you are holding a tray at waist height. The tray is not too heavy but you are carrying some weight. Put your hands in front of you, holding the imaginary tray as you sing. Don't let your body lift to reach the highest notes but maintain a feeling of being grounded.

CLOSE EVERY DOOR

MUSIC BY ANDREW LLOYD WEBBER
LYRICS BY TIM RICE

TRACK
3

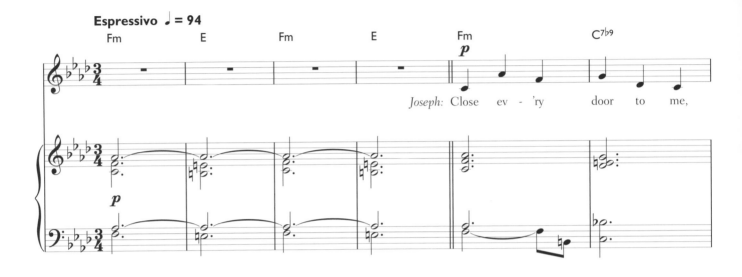

Espressivo ♩ = 94

Joseph: Close ev- 'ry door to me,

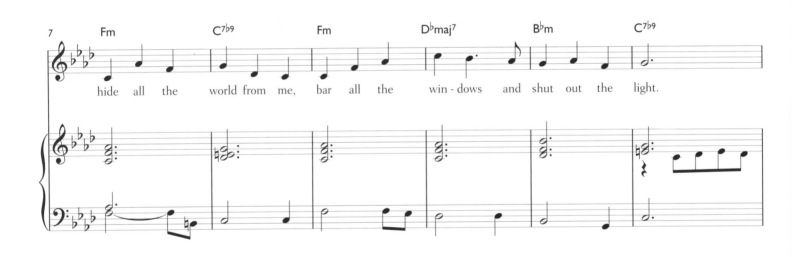

hide all the world from me, bar all the win - dows and shut out the light.

Do what you want with me, hate me and laugh at me, dark - en my day - time and

DIFFERENT

HONK!

BACKGROUND

Hans Christian Andersen's 1843 fairy tale *The Ugly Duckling* has been adapted many times as a stage show, opera, musical and animated film. *Honk!* sets the story in the English countryside and follows the adventures of Ugly as he struggles to find acceptance in a cruel world. The show was first performed in 1993 and was produced in an expanded version at the Royal National Theatre in London in 1999, winning the Olivier Award for Best Musical in 2000.

The first time Ugly meets his brother and sister ducklings they bully him mercilessly and mock him for his odd appearance. In this song, he reflects on life in the farmyard.

PERFORMANCE NOTES

Although Ugly is a bird, this song eloquently expresses the very human experience of feeling unwanted, outcast and alone in the world. He desperately wants to fit in with everyone else: he desperately wants to 'quack' (the one word he's unable to pronounce), but he can only produce a loud and ugly 'honk'.

Sometimes 'Different' is performed as a song about being sad, full of self-pity, tears and misery. Don't fall into this trap: it's a song about being *brave* – facing up to the reality of an unpleasant situation, working out why you're in it and considering what can be done to improve matters – or at least make them more bearable.

The song constantly refers to 'them', so it's important that the audience have a strong sense of the existence of those other people who don't understand or like you. You might consider inventive ways of creating a dramatic context for your performance: maybe there's a cruel joke about you chalked up on a wall? Or are you holding a favourite toy that they have broken? Or reading an article about yourself in a newspaper? Even the way you walk into the acting area will tell the audience a lot about your current level of self-esteem.

Read through the lyrics as if they are a speech. Note the changes of thought, where new ideas appear, how these are developed – and how the connotations of the word 'different' change as the song progresses. This is obviously a deeply personal and reflective song, but that doesn't necessarily mean you have to stand motionless throughout. How might some movement and gesture help you convey Ugly's growing sense of understanding and self-worth? What will you do to bring the song to an effective conclusion?

SINGING TIPS

If you read through the lyrics of this song you will see how many words contain the *n* sound, including, of course, many repetitions of the title word! Most consonants stop the flow of air and therefore the sound, but you can sustain sound through an *n* – hum an *n* and see how long you can sustain it. Now try singing 'sin' – 'sun' – 'sin' on one note holding each word for four beats. Sing into the *n* sound quickly so that the vowel is very short. Now try the same exercise but sing through the vowel, putting the *n* right at the end of the last beat. You will probably hear that, although the *n* carries the sound, the vowel gives you more. You will need to consider this when singing the word 'different', and choose the appropriate vowel sound.

DIFFERENT

WORDS BY ANTHONY DREWE
MUSIC BY GEORGE STILES

TRACK 4

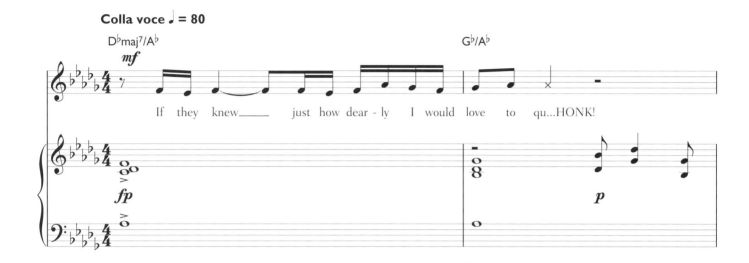

If they knew_____ just how dear-ly I would love to qu...HONK!

But it's true_____ I'm a bird who seems to lack the knack.

I'm just diff-erent,_ I'm just

FAR FROM THE HOME I LOVE
FIDDLER ON THE ROOF

BACKGROUND

Fiddler on the Roof is set in a remote Jewish village in Tsarist Russia in 1905. While the older inhabitants strongly uphold the traditions of their religion and society, Tevye the milkman struggles to keep his family together as his 5 daughters make their own way in a changing world. At the same time the army begins a programme of persecution against the Jewish community which threatens them all.

Against Tevye's wishes, his second daughter Hodel becomes engaged to a radical (and gentile) student Perchik, who is then arrested for political activity and exiled to Siberia. At the railway station Hodel explains to her father why she is leaving home to join him there.

PERFORMANCE NOTES

It's important to realise what massive risks Hodel is taking as she sets out on her journey. For a young woman to go alone – in violent and desperate times – across thousands of miles of frozen wasteland to try to find her fiancé, who may already be dead, is astonishingly brave. It's also quite possible that she will never see her father again. So for her it's absolutely essential that he understands exactly why she's taking this extraordinary step.

If you can, rehearse the scene with another actor playing Tevye. Remember that he is your father and you love him dearly. Try improvising around the scene. How do you behave on this chilly station platform? How much eye contact do you feel you can maintain? How does your relationship change as the song progresses? Focus your improvisation further by giving yourself the pressure of a time limit: the train leaves in 5 minutes, so whatever has to be said and done must happen quickly.

If you're singing this song as a solo, use what you've learnt from this exercise to inform your relationship with the audience. Although this is a 'melancholy choice', beware of lapsing into self-pity: your objective at all times is to help them understand why you must go and – as far as you can – give them some comfort.

SINGING TIPS

At the heart of this song is the interplay between the major and minor keys. The continual changing between the two mirrors Hodel's thought processes as they evolve.

Try singing up and down arpeggios, on a vowel of your choice, alternating from minor to major, slowly at first and then quicker and quicker. Then sing the first two bars of any of the minor sections of the song, followed immediately by the first two bars of a major section. Feel how the mood changes as the minor 3rd changes to a major 3rd.

Notice how often you have repeated notes at the ends of phrases. Take care that the pitch doesn't shift as you sing the different words. On one note of your choice, try singing the following: *I must travel far from home* or *Wanting to go far away*. Make up your own repeated note exercises using ideas from the song.

FAR FROM THE HOME I LOVE

WORDS BY SHELDON HARNICK
MUSIC BY JERRY BOCK

I COULD HAVE DANCED ALL NIGHT

MY FAIR LADY

BACKGROUND

My Fair Lady first appeared in New York in 1956, and went on to become a Hollywood hit. It's full of memorable songs such as 'The rain in Spain' and 'I'm getting married in the morning', which have helped to make it one of the best-loved musicals of all time. The musical is closely based on the 1914 play *Pygmalion* by English playwright George Bernard Shaw.

When Professor Henry Higgins, a pompous language expert, encounters 'guttersnipe' Eliza Doolittle selling flowers outside Covent Garden opera house he's appalled by her cockney accent and boasts to his friend Colonel Pickering that by teaching her better pronunciation he could 'pass her off as a duchess' in six months. When Eliza boldly challenges him to make good his claim, their relationship develops in ways neither of them could have predicted.

This song comes towards the end of Act 1. Higgins and Pickering have spent weeks working on Eliza's voice, endlessly making her repeat meaningless vocal exercises like 'The rain in Spain stays mainly in the plain' without success. At the end of another long, exhausting day, Eliza gives it one last try and miraculously her cockney accent disappears. The three of them sing and dance round Higgins' study in a wonderful moment of shared triumph. Shortly afterwards, when the housekeeper (Mrs Pearce) tells her it's time for bed, Eliza responds 'Bed! Bed! I couldn't go to bed!' and this song begins.

PERFORMANCE NOTES

At this point in the scene Eliza is light-headed with lack of sleep but can't contain her excitement and happiness. She suddenly senses a wonderful world of possibility where she can spread her wings and do a thousand things. You might like to compare the rather childlike dreams Eliza sings about in her first song 'Wouldn't it be loverly?' (see *Sing Musical Theatre: Wouldn't It Be Loverly?*) with the sense of lively anticipation here to consider how her character has developed over the course of the show.

The lyrics of this song are quite simple. Once the main melody begins at bar 26, Eliza repeats the same idea several times. What does this tell you about her frame of mind at this moment? What challenges and opportunities does this give you when performing the song?

SINGING TIPS

Don't be caught out in bar 26 of this song. Breathe early and hear the first note in your 'thinking' voice before you sing it. Take care to keep all those arpeggiated notes neat and even without rushing. Try the following exercise:

Slowly sing upwards arpeggios on an *ah* vowel with different consonants (eg: *dah, pah, kah, nah, lah*). Gradually increase the speed, making sure pitch and articulation remain clear. Try alternating legato and staccato. Each time you sing an arpeggio use your hands to press down gently: imagine that you're squashing a big fluffy pillow. This will help to keep your body and the sound fully connected.

I COULD HAVE DANCED ALL NIGHT

WORDS BY ALAN JAY LERNER
MUSIC BY FREDERICK LOEWE

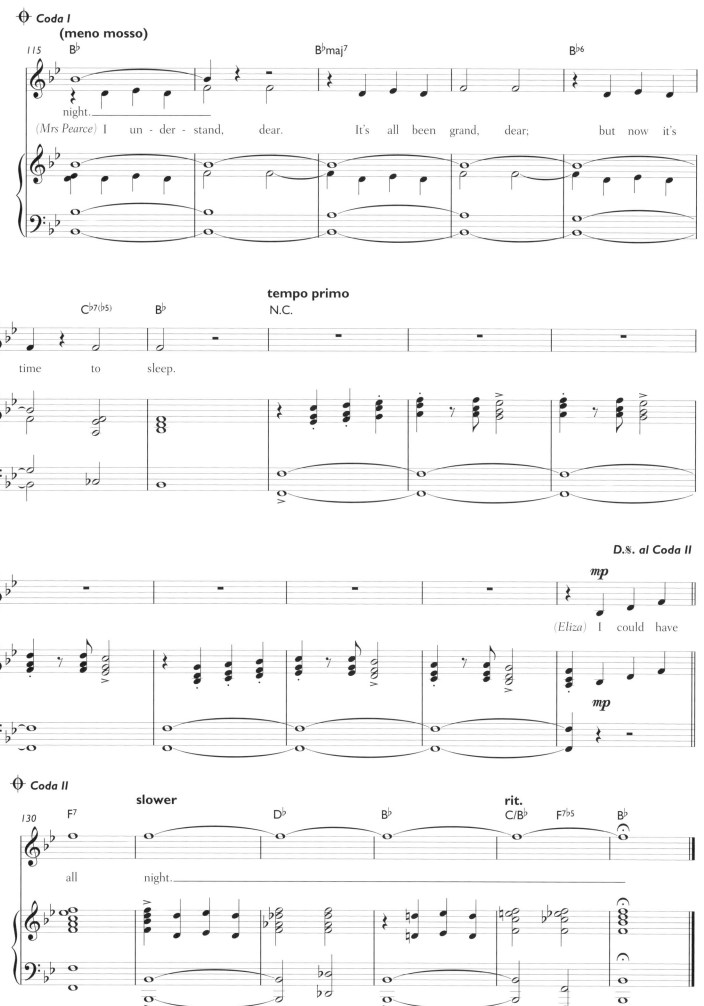

I WANT TO KNOW

BIG

BACKGROUND

The 1980s comedy-fantasy movie *Big*, starring Tom Hanks, provided the inspiration for a musical stage adaptation by Weidman, Maltby and Shire, which opened on Broadway in 1996. Although nominated for five Tony awards, the original production received mixed reviews and closed after a few months. The show was substantially re-written for the 1997 American tour, and this version continues to be produced worldwide.

12-year-old Josh Baskin longs to be grown up. A mysterious arcade game called 'Zoltar Speaks' grants him his wish and he finds himself in the body of a 30-year-old man. Josh gets a job with a toy company and is attracted to his colleague Susan. As (adult) Josh prepares to kiss her for the first time, his younger self reappears to sing 'I want to know'.

PERFORMANCE NOTES

As conceived by the writers, the staging of this song is quite complex, with 'young' Josh magically appearing to express the feelings of his older self in a moment of frozen time.

In solo performance it might be inappropriate to attempt to re-create this staging, as the presence of an 'adult' Josh will split the audience's focus and may confuse them. On the other hand, you might wish to perform with an actress playing the silent role of Susan to heighten the audience's awareness of her physical presence and your response to her. Experiment with movement in rehearsal. Does Susan have to 'freeze' as you sing the song, or are there other alternatives? Do you stay close beside her (so close you can 'feel her breath') or do you move away from her? When? Why? And for how long?

This is an awkward situation for Josh and he doesn't know how to proceed. You should resist the temptation to play the song for laughs or to be too 'cute'. The lyrics have a sense of breathless immediacy – this really is happening to you right here, right now. You are not giving the audience a comic commentary on what's happening, you're trying to work out your complex and conflicting feelings, many of which are entirely new to you.

Your thoughts are expressed with sensitivity and delicacy, an attractive self-awareness ('talked all the talk, don't know what it means'), understandable apprehension ('what happens next scares me half to death') and a true sense of wonder. Give full expression to this range of feelings to convey the enormous significance of this life-changing moment.

SINGING TIPS

In this song there are a number of arpeggiated phrases covering a wide vocal range. Try the following arpeggio exercises to help you move through these phrases:

Starting in a comfortable part of your voice, sing slowly up a major arpeggio. Sing the notes on these sounds: *You – oo – ee – ee*. Slide between the last two notes, feeling the sound opening out as you sing. Practise these arpeggios in different keys, with and then without the slide between the last two notes and then changing the vowels: try *You – ee – ah – ah*.

I WANT TO KNOW

WORDS AND MUSIC BY RICHARD MALTBY AND DAVID SHIRE

44

I'M NOT THAT GIRL

WICKED

BACKGROUND

Gregory Maguire's 1995 novel *Wicked* retells the story of *The Wizard of Oz* through the eyes of Elphaba, the Wicked Witch of the West. The book provided the inspiration for the musical *Wicked*, which opened on Broadway in 2003. The show rapidly established itself as a massive hit. It broke box office records everywhere and – to date – is the most successful new musical of the 21st century.

Shy, awkward and green-skinned, Elphaba is constantly outshone by her university room-mate, the ultra-popular, blonde, glamorous Galinda. Both girls are attracted to their fellow student, the dashing Prince Fiyero. Outraged by the university's use of animals for scientific experiments, Elphaba and Fiyero steal a lion cub from the laboratory and set it free. But despite their growing friendship, Elphaba knows that Galinda is the girl Fiyero loves and – inevitably – will marry.

PERFORMANCE NOTES

A huge amount happens to Elphaba and Fiyero immediately before this song: the shared thrill of the night-time robbery, the release of the lion, a brief tender moment as they hide under a bridge. But he has just left, embarrassed, and now you have to take stock of where you are.

Use the four opening bars to think about what has happened and establish the mood. As you start to sing, remember that the sensations you describe are entirely new to you ('sudden heat', 'giddy whirl') and they are exciting, strange and magical. But this enchanted moment can't last. You're a realist and you know it's dangerous to 'dream too far'. Don't use the song to wallow in self-pity; use it to demonstrate your integrity and clear-sighted honesty about yourself, your friends and your feelings.

The final verse has a slightly different tone. Why do you feel the need to repeat those warnings to yourself ('don't wish, don't start')? Note how the last three lines give a bald summary of the situation: Galinda, Fiyero, yourself. What do you hope to achieve in making this final statement? How have your feelings changed by the end of the song?

SINGING TIPS

Some of this song lies quite low in the voice. Try the following exercises to practise lower register sounds: Imagine that you are Santa Claus. You're laughing – *ho, ho, ho!* Do this in a really low part of your voice, using plenty of tone. You may feel some vibration in your chest as you do this.

Now, towards the bottom end of your range, sing five notes of a descending scale, each one to the word *new*. Exaggerate the sound at the beginning of the word so that the word becomes *nnneeyou*. Almost hum through the *n* sound and feel a hint of pressure behind the nose. Don't necessarily aim for a really beautiful sound – go for one that's really resonant.

Remember that you don't need to push the sound out. Keep the air flowing freely and avoid too much tension in your body. Don't let your head drop as you sing lower!

I'M NOT THAT GIRL

MUSIC AND LYRICS BY STEPHEN SCHWARTZ

Sweet and steady, like a music box ♩ = 96

Hands touch,_ eyes meet,_ sud-den si - lence,

sud-den heat._ Heart leap_ in a gid-dy whirl, he could be that boy,_____

MISTER SNOW

CAROUSEL

BACKGROUND

Carousel opened on Broadway in 1945. With its tragic plot, complex leading characters, innovative structure and heavily integrated use of singing, drama and dance, it is now recognised as a key work in the development of 20th-century musical theatre, and has influenced generations of writers, composers, choreographers and directors.

The show is set in a small New England town in the late 19th century. When Julie Jordan and Carrie Pipperidge, two young mill workers, visit a travelling carnival, Julie catches the eye of the barker Billy Bigelow and falls in love with him. Delighted that her friend has at long last found a 'fellah', Carrie tells her about her own fiancé.

PERFORMANCE NOTES

'I been bustin' to tell you something lately', Carrie tells Julie as the song begins. It's important to remember that Carrie has had to keep her relationship with Mr Snow a secret, but finally she's able to tell her best friend all about it. If you're performing the song as a solo, treat the audience in the same way – they're your confidantes, you can trust them entirely, and they'll want to share your happiness.

Note how Carrie describes Mr Snow with a mixture of pride, apprehension and humour. He's an 'upstanding man' with his own boat and modest business, an 'almost perfect beau' if it weren't for his permanent aroma of fish. But you can afford to make a joke about this – after all, you're confident, cheerful, optimistic and in love. Once she gets started, Carrie can't resist telling Julie the whole story from the beginning. Make sure you mark carefully the various stages of their relationship. Why do you think Carrie quotes Mr Snow directly in the following section, reproducing his rather awkward proposal word for word? What impression do you get of him in this scene? His age? His outlook?

The last section moves into the future and the 'day of days'. There's a great deal of dramatic and comic potential here. Consider, for instance, the impression you want to give when 'kinda sweet[ly]' you say 'Well, Mr Snow, here I am' on your wedding day – the only time you speak directly to him in the song. Then really enjoy the rising phrases as you make a final list of your wonderful fiancé's qualities: 'darling Mister Snow' indeed.

SINGING TIPS

Plenty of acting with the voice is needed in this song. You have to 'paint' a picture of Mr Snow as well as communicate Carrie's excitement. Try singing with a feeling of inner laughter and energy, keeping the phrases moving forward through the quavers but never rushing.

You may well choose to sing in an American accent. First though, try singing with a really exaggerated 'posh' accent. Feel how hard your lips and tongue have to work to articulate the sounds. Now sing through a section of the song trying not to move your lips or tongue very much at all. You'll notice how hard it is to communicate the words. You should be aiming to work the muscles, but not overwork them. Practise in front of a mirror to see the shapes you're making.

MISTER SNOW

LYRICS BY OSCAR HAMMERSTEIN II
MUSIC BY RICHARD RODGERS

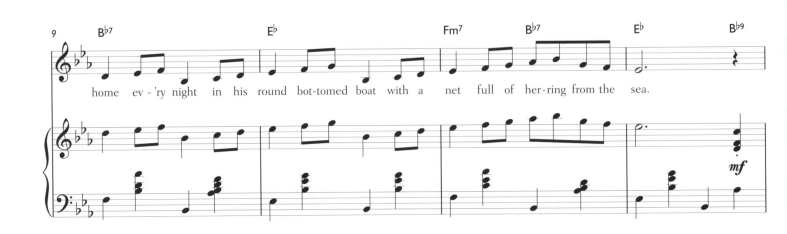

56

OH, THE RIO GRANDE

JOHNNY JOHNSON

BACKGROUND

The German-born composer Kurt Weill (1900–50) holds a unique place in the history of 20th century musical theatre. After early musical and operatic successes in Europe he was forced to flee the Nazis in 1933, eventually making his home in America, where he enjoyed a second career writing Broadway musicals. Weill was a committed socialist who believed that writing music should have a socially useful purpose, and most of his works have a strong political element.

Johnny Johnson, the story of an American soldier's traumatic experiences in World War I, was Weill's first Broadway show. In this song, an American soldier in the trenches dreams of home.

PERFORMANCE NOTES

This song is the dream of a soldier in a strange land longing for freedom and space, for a land where 'the wind blows free' and the cowboy rides proudly across the prairies. For both the soldier and his comrades who are listening, it's an escape which can momentarily transport them from their appalling present situation to a better world. Although you may choose not to perform the song in role as a soldier, aim to provide your audience with the same kind of inspiration and hope.

Enjoy the rolling rhythm and expansive melody of the refrain. Visualise the landscape and share those images of vast, sun-filled plains with the single shadow of horse and rider skimming across the grass.

Of course this is the life that your 'gal' insists that you must give up before she will marry you. Make sure the next part of the story is very clear – your dull, unsatisfactory life together, the trip to the rodeo, your triumphant announcement of your plan to head for Texas. Punch out the words 'I am bound': let us really know you've made that decision.

The broad melody of the refrain now returns, as do the images of freedom on the rolling plains. But as the final line tells us, the difference is that now 'my gal rides at my side'. Together sharing a common destiny, the two of you disappear into the sunset – literally – heading for a brighter future.

SINGING TIPS

This song requires good diction but also a feel of swing. To get your tongue and lips working try the following:

Say *tick, tock, tick, tock* a few times and then say *click, clock, click, clock*. Make it as rhythmic as you can. Alternate between the two, seeing how fast you can get without becoming tongue-tied.

On one note, sing the words: *papa, papa, papa, papa, doo*. As you sing, crescendo through the phrase and really feel the lips working.

Don't forget to feel the syncopation in the song. Clap your hands to establish a pulse and then practise speaking the 'Oh, the Rio Grande' sections out loud, making sure the rhythms are neat and crisp.

OH, THE RIO GRANDE

LYRICS BY PAUL GREEN
MUSIC BY KURT WEILL

TRACK
10

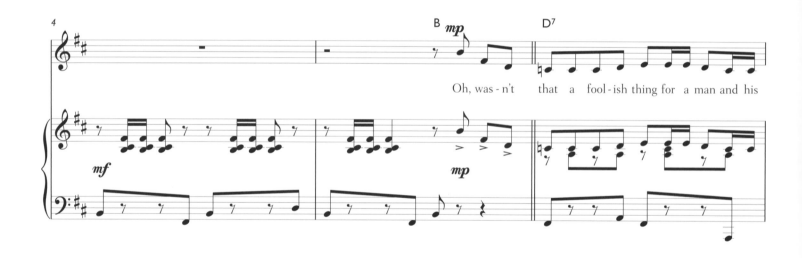

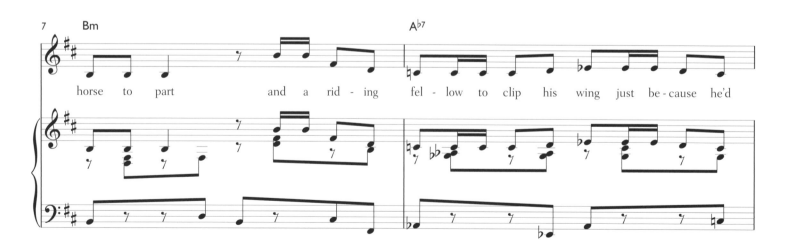

OOM PAH PAH

OLIVER!

BACKGROUND

Lionel Bart's musical adaptation of Charles Dickens' 1838 novel *Oliver Twist* was an immediate hit when it was first performed in London in 1963. With its classic storyline, tuneful music hall-influenced score and cast of colourful London characters, it remains one of the few truly British musicals to have established itself as a firm favourite with audiences all over the world.

The story is set in London in the early 19th century and follows the adventures of young orphan Oliver Twist as he's thrown out of a workhouse and falls into the clutches of the villainous Fagin and his terrifying accomplice Bill Sykes. Only Nancy, Bill's long-suffering girlfriend, shows Oliver any kindness and eventually helps him to escape – with tragic consequences for herself. At the opening of Act 2, Nancy sings 'Oom pah pah' to the patrons of the Three Cripples pub.

PERFORMANCE NOTES

This is a boisterous sing-along pub song, with Nancy as master (or mistress) of ceremonies leading the crowd and encouraging everybody to have a good time. The lyrics are mildly suggestive – we're not told exactly what 'oom pah pah' refers to – but everybody will 'suppose what they want to suppose' when they hear the phrase. When you're performing this song you should enjoy sharing this rather 'saucy' secret with the audience.

This is a great song to work on with a group. The pub scene can be set up easily with a few tables and chairs, and everyone can develop their own characters within it. Nancy can lead the song, or the verses can be taken by different performers. The waltz rhythm will support group movement or choreography, particularly in the choruses, leading to a raucous finale. If you're performing the song as a solo, consider the implications for Nancy herself. Though we know very little about her background, the tale of 'pretty little Sally' who got 'up a gum tree' (became pregnant) and who is now 'glad to bring the coin in' (making her living – and possibly supporting both the baby and its father – as a prostitute) mirrors her own situation in many ways. She is no longer 'the same blushing rose' she once was.

SINGING TIPS

This is a great song to practise with movement. The drive in the music comes from the strong beat at the beginning of each bar.

As you're practising, try singing and pacing, moving forward, sideways or even backwards (carefully!) on every strong beat. Add some arm movements, making sure you always stay on the beat.

Try stressing the 'oom' each time you sing 'oom pah pah'. You might want to try a glottal stop for this. Try saying *uh-oh* as if something has just gone wrong. Can you feel how the sound is stopped between the *uh* and the *oh*? Exaggerate this and you'll really feel it. This is a glottal stop. Now try it as you sing 'oom' and you'll get a strong start to the sound, which will help to give the first beat of the bar lots of energy. This glottal stop will also help with the cockney accent. Notice that words like 'ditty' and 'city' don't have the *t* sound in the middle of them: it's replaced by a glottal stop between the *i* and the *y* sounds.

OOM PAH PAH

WORDS AND MUSIC BY LIONEL BART

TRACK
11

THERE MUST BE MORE

GRACE ONLINE

BACKGROUND

Grace Online was first performed by Youth Music Theatre UK[†] in 2007. Sixteen-year-old Grace lives in a provincial town with her strict, ultra-religious parents who insist on schooling her at home. Bored and isolated, she starts exploring social networks on the internet and when she launches a website offering support and advice, 'supercute, supersmart' Grace becomes a guru to thousands of teenagers worldwide. Her parents remain unaware of her online celebrity status however, and when she leaves the house without their permission they confine her to her bedroom for a week as punishment.

PERFORMANCE NOTES

A teenager sits in her bedroom, moaning about her parents' 'stupid rules', complaining that she feels like she's in prison. It is important you make this all-too-familiar setting clear to the audience in the opening few lines through your attitude, staging and body language because almost immediately the song sets off in a new, unexpected direction.

Use the swooping melody and fragmented lyrics (which jump rapidly from yourself to 'others', from your own cramped environment to the wider world beyond 'this bedroom door') to give expression both to your gnawing frustration and to your hope that one day you will 'fly away' and experience freedom. (You might like to compare the song to 'Somewhere over the rainbow' from *The Wizard of Oz*.) 'But' – surprisingly – 'for now, it's okay'. While Dorothy is stuck alone on her farm in Kansas, Grace is a twenty-first-century girl with access to the internet and 'a thousand friends online'. How does your mood change in the sections when you sing about your site, your parents, Daniel and so on? How much comfort does the thought of all those other people out there in cyberspace give you? And how might you make this clear to the audience in performance?

If you are working with a group, you might use the haunting melody and repeated chorus as the basis for some solo, pair or group movement work to explore ideas of communication, friendship and loneliness. In the original production the entire cast sang the final verse to convey the sense that 'There must be more' is a deeply-felt human sentiment that we all share. How might you convey something of this in solo performance?

SINGING TIPS

This song has very distinct sections, each marked with a different tempo direction and each presenting different challenges. Bars 1, 2, 15 and 16 are almost conversational in style, following the rhythm patterns of ordinary speech. Practise these passages very slowly at first in strict rhythm and then, when you feel you know the words, try allowing them to sound quite free. Don't play around with the rhythms too much. At the *più mosso* section, as the speed increases, you have to fit with a very busy accompaniment, so practise with a keen sense of underlying pulse. As you're practising, try singing and pacing, moving forward, sideways or even backwards (carefully!) on every strong beat. Add some arm movements, making sure you always stay on the beat. Finally, as the song ends, really think about the impact of the final *rall*.

[†] Youth Music Theatre UK was founded in 2003 and is now Britain's largest organisation providing participation in musical theatre projects and productions for young people. For more information about Youth Music Theatre UK, its Musical Theatre Library and how to perform this work, go to www.youthmusictheatreuk.org.

THERE MUST BE MORE

WORDS AND MUSIC BY GARTH MCCONAGHIE

Why do my pa-rents make these stu-pid rules? My life's spent on a lap-top, I can't e-ven go to school. My

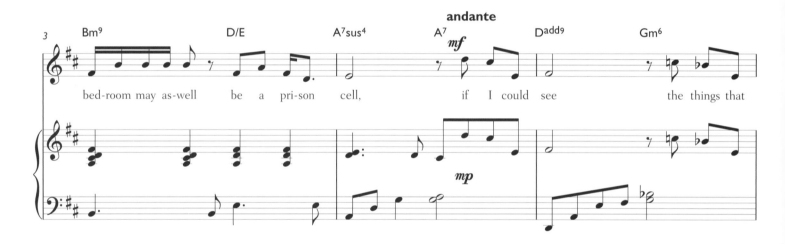

bed-room may as-well be a pri-son cell, if I could see the things that

o-thers see I'd find my way, if I were free. There must be

WHEN I GET MY NAME IN LIGHTS
THE BOY FROM OZ

BACKGROUND

The Boy from Oz tells the life story of Peter Allen, the popular Australian entertainer and songwriter who enjoyed international success in the 1970s and 1980s, marrying Liza Minnelli and winning an Oscar for 'Arthur's Theme' before his premature death at the age of 48 in 1992. After playing to over a million people on tour from Sydney to Perth, *The Boy from Oz* became the first home-grown Australian musical to open on Broadway, running for two years with Hugh Jackman in the title role.

In this song, eight-year-old Peter entertains his mother and her friends by singing and dancing round their living room in sleepy Tenterfield, New South Wales.

PERFORMANCE NOTES

As performed in the show, *When I Get My Name in Lights* is an astonishingly accomplished song-and-dance number performed by a precociously talented young boy. Unlike many musical theatre songs in which characters speculate on what the future will bring, here there is no anxiety, no self-doubt. It's all about 'when' – not 'if' – you're going to see your name in lights. You may even wish to further demonstrate your all-round world-beating talents by repeating a couple of verses for a tap dance solo before the big finish.

In the show, this living-room performance occurs in flashback, introduced and observed by the adult Peter. Given all the ups and downs that he has experienced in a lifetime in showbiz, how do you think he might feel about his childhood self and those big, easy dreams? And how might adult Peter's presence modify the audience's reaction to the song?

An older performer might wish to consider the deeper implications of some of the lyrics to create a more rounded, adult character. The opening rubato section suggests that something has happened in the past to prevent you from reaching your potential but now you are 'free as a breeze again'. Why might that be? Use the bright tune and upbeat lyrics to move the song relentlessly forward, a big smile on your face. But what might that smile hide? Do you really believe that fame can happen overnight with a change of hair-do? What do you really think about the craziness of the modern world? Why do you have to keep re-stating your desire for fame at any cost (you'll even 'sit on a flagpole') over and over again? And to what extent might this extremely positive song represent a denial of experience, an escape from the responsibilities of your everyday life?

SINGING TIPS

This is a high-energy dance performance number, so even when you are just learning the song, practise moving around, flinging the arms wide or swinging them backwards and forwards. With such a lot going on in this very rhythmic song, the words need to remain crisp and clear as you move around. Try the following exercises:

Set up a 4-in-a-bar beat, either by clapping the beats or marching on the spot. Say

Think of the tip of the tongue.

Repeat this a couple of times. Then, continuing to mark out your count of four, try:

Lo-ver-ly lips to loo-sen up.

Then alternate between the two phrases, always keeping the pulse steady and the words clear.

WHEN I GET MY NAME IN LIGHTS

WORDS AND MUSIC BY PETER ALLEN

TRACK 13

WHEN I LOOK AT YOU
THE SCARLET PIMPERNEL

BACKGROUND

Baroness Orczy's swashbuckling adventure novel *The Scarlet Pimpernel* was a worldwide success on its publication in 1905 and has since provided the basis for numerous sequels, adaptations and parodies in print, movies, books and on TV. The hero – who achieves superhuman feats while concealing his true identity behind a mild-mannered alter ego – is a precursor of superheroes such as Zorro, Superman and Batman.

Shortly after his marriage to Marguerite St Just, dashing English aristocrat Percy Blakeney adopts the persona of an obnoxious, dandified fop to conceal the fact that he is in reality The Scarlet Pimpernel, a mysterious adventurer who saves victims of the French Revolution from the guillotine. Marguerite is unaware of his double life and is mystified by the radical change in his personality. As Percy sits for his portrait, she reflects on his transformation.

PERFORMANCE NOTES

There are three characters within this song: 'I' – the mystified singer; 'you' – the repellent man you now see in front of you; and 'him', the wonderful individual with whom you fell in love long ago. It's a complicated tangle of personalities because 'you' and 'him' are of course the same person, something which the audience has to understand from the outset.

In a fully staged production, Marguerite can make reference both to Percy sitting for his portrait and to the painting itself to help clarify the lyrics. What alternative props and staging might you use to convey the essence of the dramatic situation in a solo performance? A wedding photograph? A piece of jewellery or treasured gift? A pile of love letters?

As the song progresses and you struggle to understand why 'you' can't be 'him' again, notice how the words get mixed up: 'you were once that someone ... then you changed'. The two men seem momentarily to blend into one. Who is who? Whose fault is this? Your own? ('Did I create a dream?') What's going on? Of course the real confusion stems from the fact that all this is an act. Percy hasn't actually changed at all – he's still the charming, wonderful man he always was – and everything will be made clear by the time the curtain falls. But at this stage in the story there are no answers for Marguerite and she ends the song with only her memories, bereft and alone.

SINGING TIPS

This is a reflective song that is nevertheless very passionate and emotional. A good way to prepare for this is to play with different dynamics and colours to highlight the moods.

Don't start too loud or you'll have no sense of build-up through the song. Think of quieter singing, retaining high energy and projection, and don't make your mouth too small or this will hold the sound back. Imagine a small candle flame in a dark room. The candle is some distance from you and you need to focus the sound as you sing through the darkness to that point of light. As you open out into the stronger sections of the song, imagine all the lights coming on in the room and feel the sound filling the space. To ensure that you have plenty of resonance in the sound, try singing *mini-me* on each note of an ascending and descending scale.

WHEN I LOOK AT YOU

WORDS BY NAN KNIGHTON
MUSIC BY FRANK WILDHORN

TRACK
14

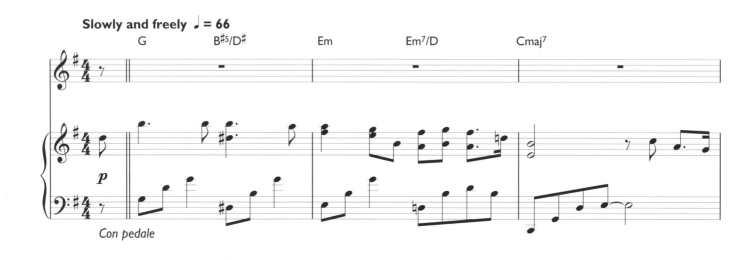

WHISTLE DOWN THE WIND
WHISTLE DOWN THE WIND

BACKGROUND

Whistle Down the Wind – a story about a group of Lancashire schoolchildren who discover an escaped convict in a barn and mistakenly assume he is Jesus Christ – started life as novel by Mary Ann Bell but became more widely known through the classic 1961 film starring Alan Bates and Hayley Mills. The 1996 musical version by Andrew Lloyd Webber and Jim Steinman transferred the action to Louisiana but retained the core story, characters and 1950s small-town setting.

Swallow, her younger sister Brat and brother Poor Baby have lost their mother a few months previously. Their father Boone does his best to keep the family together and reminds them of the song their mother used to sing to comfort them in bad times.

PERFORMANCE NOTES

This is a song of reassurance; a quiet, simple lullaby that builds into a bold statement of friendship, love and total commitment. Its sentiments are broad, its lyrics not directly related to a single dramatic situation so – as always with musical theatre songs – it's important to make a decision about who you are singing to, so your performance remains focused and precise. The choice is yours: a child? A friend? A lover? A parent? What exactly might a line like 'I'll be there to hold you' mean in relation to those different people? Aim always to be specific and clear in your thinking – never vague and generalised – and use this to inform your delivery of the lyrics.

As you sing, relish the richness and mystery of the words. What do you understand by the phrase 'whistle down the wind'? Why do you think it is the title of the story? Note how the lyrics move from 'a patch of darkness', up to the stars in the heavens and then – heroically – to images of raising a banner and building a bonfire as a beacon of hope. Envisage these scenes as you sing and paint them vividly for your audience.

The song ends with an intimate moment and re-statement of the unshakeable bond between you and the person to whom you are singing. What effect do you want the song to have on your 'precious friend'? Is that the same as its effect on the audience?

SINGING TIPS

Set a speed for this song that gives you a sense of flow, and don't let your energy levels drop in the lyrical sections. Before you start to sing, jog on the spot for a moment, wriggle the wrists and swivel the hips to get the body engaged but loose.

With a sense of the musical line travelling forward, still take time to bring out the important words. There are many repeated notes and rhythms that need shape and variety of colour here, so think about how to characterise words such as 'scary', 'howl', 'whisper', 'stop' and 'precious'. You can lengthen or shorten some of the quavers slightly, but try not to cut the longer held notes at ends of phrases too short or you'll lose the feeling of momentum. To practise sustaining notes that still feel energised try singing on a note of your choice, counting through 6 beats in your head while drawing a big circle and then a Catherine wheel shape that starts small and gets bigger and bigger. Ensure that you're producing a lovely even sound while you draw.

WHISTLE DOWN THE WIND

MUSIC BY ANDREW LLOYD WEBBER
LYRICS BY JIM STEINMAN

TRACK
15

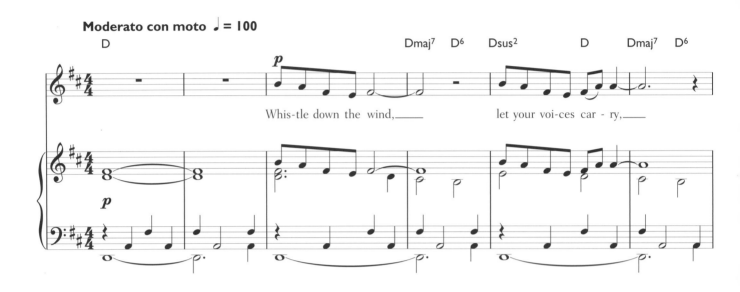

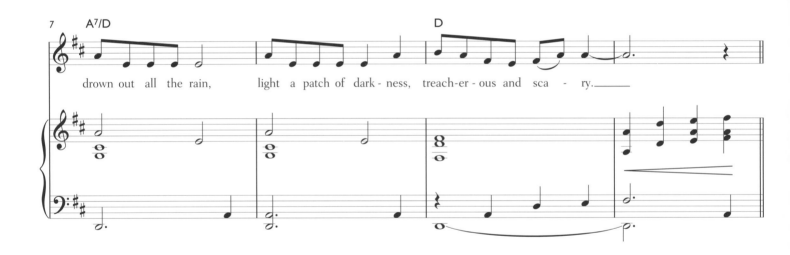

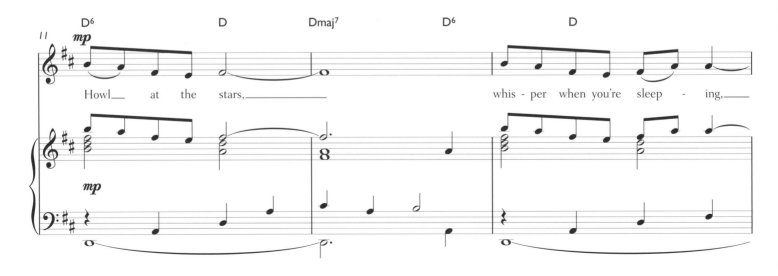

OTHER TITLES AVAILABLE IN THIS SERIES

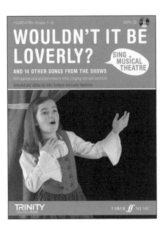

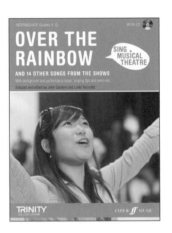

ANY DREAM WILL DO

ISBN10: 0-571-53555-0

ANY DREAM WILL DO

BE KIND TO YOUR PARENTS

A COMMON BOY

FAT SAM'S GRAND SLAM

FLASH, BANG, WALLOP!

JUST ONE PERSON

LET'S GO FLY A KITE

A LOVELY LEGGY POTION

MAYBE

MOONSHINE LULLABY

MY FAVOURITE THINGS

PART OF YOUR WORLD

ROUND-SHOULDERED MAN

THE WASPISH TANGO

WHERE IS LOVE?

WOULDN'T IT BE LOVERLY

ISBN10: 0-571-53556-9

A PLACE CALLED NEVERLAND

A SPOONFUL OF SUGAR

ALONE IN THE UNIVERSE

COLDER NOW

CURIOUSER

I WANT TO BE HAPPY

IT'S A LOVELY DAY TODAY

MR MISTOFFELEES

NO ONE KNOWS WHO I AM

SO YOU WANNA BE A BOXER

THE GIRL I MEAN TO BE

UNDER THE SEA

WE'RE OFF TO SEE THE WIZARD

WHO WILL BUY?

WOULDN'T IT BE LOVERLY?

OVER THE RAINBOW

ISBN10: 0-571-53557-7

BEAUTIFUL

FEED THE BIRDS

I CAN HEAR THE BELLS

I LOVE PARIS

I WANT TO GO HOME

LEGALLY BLONDE

LES POISSONS

MY DEFENCES ARE DOWN

MY SHIP

NOTICE ME, HORTON

ONLY LOVE

OVER THE RAINBOW

REVIEWING THE SITUATION

SOMETHING GOOD

WARTS AND ALL

To buy Faber Music or Trinity publications or to find out about the full range of titles available
please contact your local music retailer or Faber Music sales enquiries:

Faber Music Ltd, Burnt Mill, Elizabeth Way, Harlow CM20 2HX
Tel: +44 (0) 1279 82 89 89   Fax: +44 (0) 1279 82 89 90
sales@fabermusic.com   fabermusic.com   fabermusicstore.com